MY LITTLE BROTHER

Christel Wiinblad was born in 1980 in Svendborg, Denmark. She has published four collections of poetry; *49 Forelskelser* (2008), *Min lillebror – en morgen i himlen, ihvertfald i det grønne* (2008), *Det ligner en sorg* (2011) and *Sommerlys* (2013), and three novels; *Prolog* (2011), *Ingen åbner* (2012) and *De elskende* (2014).

Malene Engelund was born in 1980 in Aalborg, Denmark. She holds an MA in Creative Writing from Royal Holloway, University of London, and her debut pamphlet *The Wild Gods* was published by Valley Press in 2016. She lives in Copenhagen.

My Little Brother

a morning in heaven, at least in green

CHRISTEL WIINBLAD

Translated by
MALENE ENGELUND

Valley Press

First published in 2020 by Valley Press
Woodend, The Crescent, Scarborough, YO11 2PW
www.valleypressuk.com

First edition, first printing (January 2020)

ISBN 978-1-912436-35-4
Cat. no. VP0155

Cover and text design by Jamie McGarry.
Cover illustration by Anita Wiinblad.

Printed and bound in the EU by Pulsio, Paris.

This translation was supported by the

DANISH ARTS FOUNDATION

Contents

17 Louisenlund, 2nd March 1984

07.52.27 am: They left an hour ago and in nine hours, five minutes and thirty seconds he'll let off his first scream. 09.34.30 am: In thirteen years and two days, the pack of firecrackers he bought with his birthday money, tucked into the inner pocket of his cotton coat along with eight and a half Mayfair and a disposable blue lighter, will set alight and he'll throw himself into the snow as if on fire. 09.45.31: My mother begins screaming and in a few days I'll push my finger into his small, clutched hand for the first time, it being only eight and a half years until he shoots me down in the garden with his new plastic revolver, before I hit him on the head with a spade and he hits back with a broom. 11.11.04 am: In five hours his head crowns, and in two months I'll throw him into the bin before my mum picks him up and I'm allowed to diaper him. 1.58.03 pm: In three hours they'll place him onto her chest and in twelve years I'll hit him, this time with a shovel, so that he passes out before he has the chance to hit back or start crying. 2.02.38 pm: I'm already waiting to see those wonderful eyes of his when, in about two years, he'll get a push car for Christmas and speed around my grandmother's apartment making indents into the wallpaper, before they finally manage to stop him and put him to bed. 2.15.16 pm: I'll soon learn that he almost never cries; instead he sucks his right thumb which will still be at least one centimetre shorter than the other when he in twenty two years turns twenty two and no longer looks like himself, and already fifteen years from now, his five fingers will reach past mine and it'll then be three years since he stopped sleeping on the crackling plastic sheet. 5.00.01 pm: The midwife sucks him out. He's been rushing and his left shoulder is stuck. Soon the rest of him will follow, they'll cut the chord and he releases a beautiful stream of piss onto the doctor who, in a few hours, will tell my mum that her son is paralysed on his left side; she'll panic although in seven weeks it'll pass.

Copenhagen Central Station, 13th January 2006

I almost fall
in beneath my black hat, then out
of the electric warmth of the carriage, and into
the platform air

amongst cigarettes and beanies, and I wonder
how the production of anti-psychotic medicine
really smells; here in the snow,
between the trains, only my nose
recalls summer
while the wind hisses and huddles

underneath the awning, where a woman,
shivering on the bench,
solves a crossword puzzle in the cold
with a blunt pencil
that spreads her unreadable writing across
the black borders
of the small white squares,

and by the main entrance, the pigeons whirl
before diving softly
as if for salt in the snowdrifts
underneath the digital clock,
that releases drops of red

numbers from the roof onto me,
stood here in the foyer, once again
far too early,

before I pull the door open
to the cold at Vesterbrogade,

and only the buildings,
the routes,
and something even more unknown
seem familiar enough
for me to feel as home

as I am,
and only a moment ago

I believed that the footprints
I'm wading through, slipping in,
belonged to my little brother, but he's of course home in Funen
and he never wears cowboy boots anyway, and right now
it's exactly six months before

he'll be placed
in a bed with the white room's
soft imprint surrounding him
like a temporary container,
at the hospital near
the graveyard
behind the railway tracks
in Svendborg.

My mother will step through the door
that shuts the lid of the container to, and now
he's the grasshopper,
and it yells
because she's been crying
and he wishes for a head
as simple as that of a horse,
that of a tree,

while I like now (but wearing a summer dress
and bare feet
in my sandals), am running diagonally
across the junction

to understand
if the cars dare hit me,
before I grab my bike
that's been left on Vester Voldgade
underneath the clock's milk-covered dial.

Gammel Strand, 13th February 2006

the storm has hurled
roof tiles and bikes through the ice
and ripped it even further open

than the long incisions
that in five months will be placed lengthwise
on both of my little brother's wrists
because, that morning, he'll believe

that he really means what
he's drunk enough
to do

to finally be permitted
to be quiet,
dizzy away
and just sleep peacefully
out of the world
and himself,

but right now
not much is happening
apart from two antennae, an Asda-bag and three pairs of ducks
floating around the soup underneath the railing

I'm walking on, while a hunched man in a red coat
and intensely white-glowing hair,
throws empty bottles into a skip,
and now it's a big wide-screen TV
he, howling and angry,

throws into
one of the mouths of the canal
that looks like the hole the just dead leaves in the world
and in a brief, passing time warp
can peep through

to study what's
there,
which is as distant
as that morning seventeen years ago

when my little brother and I
cycled with each other's foot soles as pedals on the sofa,
listening to Sgt. Pepper, Treasure Island
and Jacques Brel,

and I'm cold
because I've lost my gloves,
and already now I'm upset
that in five months and a week I'll forget
to buy the tennis wristbands
that we carefully,
together,

were meant to pull onto his wrists
to hide
what he'd almost done
a few days earlier;

my fever will have eased
but my stomach will still not settle,
and already here on the bridge
I'm wishing that in this moment
I'll have met the people
who will hold the world in place –
the kind of safe pegs
I haven't found yet
but who'll appear
and become my gentle acquaintances
in all these situations
I'm supposed
to find myself in.

The bridge lets go,
my boots lose their grip

of the railings I now bang my head against,
and what is it I really think
I know
when I don't know
what I can do

to prevent that
which I know,

and I land
onto the pavement, but I'm not the one
who feels like disappearing

before the sun rises in a few hours
and I can suddenly remember
that I've walked outside because I dreamt
that I couldn't throw up –
couldn't extract the raw chicken I'd
eaten from within myself again.

The TV descends,
the man whoops and I wonder
how many people right now
are close to falling out of a window,
wonder how long it'll take
before someone gives in
and throws loose change
from the top of the Eiffel Tower,
ashamed
of their desire

to kill at least one random tourist,
but now, this very moment
is made of clouds and orange peel
generously, delicately sowed
by someone across the sky,

while I get up and notice
that there by the statue of the Fishwife on Gammel Strand,
a man is lying with his shirt above his head,
collapsed on the cobbles, and next to him
a woman with greasy hair
is slumped over
a flat Special Brew.

Her pyjamas shirt
shines optimistically like dandruff and spit over the dirty dress
whose skirt is now unfolded by a wind
that either reaches for her knickers
or attempts to dress her in a tutu,

and meanwhile my little brother's asleep
in his own bed on Funen, unsettled
and haunted by nightmares, and again tonight when he walks
    home
from the park where he's been playing hacky-sack with the
    others in the snow,
he'll feel like climbing onto the roof of the town hall
only to fall

down,
and I think of the stitches
that'll soon close

his wrists, and in summer
it'll be summer, and in January
nothing much will be lost
apart from the mobile he'll leave
in the woods, instead

he'll finally manage
to wake up with all his secrets opened,
bled out,
smeared
and spread
onto the grass in the summer sun.

Kongens Have, 13th March 2006

four months from now, a fog seeps through the window crack,
into my ear, and further, further down
into my heart
with a blast

whose echo already reverberates threateningly
as if it's at random thrown back and forth
between the tree trunks here in Kongens Have

where the chains of my footprints,
placed precisely heel to toe,
repeat themselves neatly
in symmetrical patterns
round and round

the paths, while my little brother is in Christiansminde
in Svendborg, watching the ships,
the ducks
and all the stones,
that lay here too when he was a boy
and ate most of the bread himself,
but now he hardly ever eats.

And he then discards his cigarette,
because he needs to take a piss,
and walks up among the trees, right there
where my mother, a quiet spring morning at 5 am
almost forty years ago, found a man

who'd shot himself in the head,
through his mouth,
and the gun, smudged and soaked with blood and spit,
lay abandoned on the footpath, aiming at her, and today

it's eleven days since
my little brother turned twenty two
and I gave him a yellow baby canary
because it was already happening then,
and a bit of singing perhaps couldn't prevent it,

but at least prolong the pain – push July
onto the other side of December,
because who can leave
a small singing bird.

But it's pointless,
so perhaps he should've just stayed with Mike in New York
(where he'll go in June)
because then, in four months,
he won't go to the woods
behind my mother's house

with razors in his pocket
and letters and vintage port in his rucksack (his school bag (the
flowered one))
and no longer be all dressed up
as himself,
but still he'll smell

of sweat and tobacco
and also a bit
of the heart shaped soap
I kept on my windowsill
twenty years ago
to fill the room

with flowers and fruit,
birds and flight,
and something really pretty
like lavender and curry-yellowed silk

has landed in the bed on the lawn
by the castle, shot up
from the earth, up
through the snow
side by side

with cigarette butts,
beer tops
and small notes
with phone numbers and library receipts –

and there they are,
straight and happy in the snow,
waiting

to wither
because finally

summer returns, but why
then does he cut into his wounds again and again, each time
he comes to
in yet another (almost new)
kind of failure
not to be
dead, before

he hears some girls skipping in a garden
and Andreas screaming his name some place further up the rail
    tracks,
and finally he gives up and walks home,
but right now
is still a place
between winter and spring and I sit down on the bench

next to an old man
sleeping with his coat unbuttoned
and mouth open,

and I look past his false teeth
that have fallen onto his bottom lip,
past the dry, greying,
yellow-specked tongue
into a great black hole –

and behind him
(there, by the fountain), a small girl
is carefully placing two paper boats onto the ice,
and at each bow,
two small figures;

a little brother and his big sister lost at sea
as if frozen stiff
and so, unable
to move
yet and now
he spits his false teeth into the bin
while he sings, unfolds his legs
and I find the note
in my pocket:

checklist:
- white flannel bands for the wrists (preferably w/o logo)
- cartons of organic apple juice
- dark sugar-free chocolate
- Bachelard's *The Flame of a Candle* (which preferably I need back)
- Bolaño's *The Savage Detectives* (the burgundy paperback edition)
- an E-string
- The new book by Peter Adolphsen (the one about the little horse with the oil heart that must surely have been released in July)
- Thom Yorke's new album (*The Eraser* (released in the beginning of July, but I'll already have been given it by a friend of mine for my birthday mid-June))
- The Kitty Blue-Eyes book
- Tobacco (brand? remember to ask)
- 1 pack of Rizla (buy two)

but although I've already written it down now
I still can't avoid that in four months and that number of days,
I'll still have forgotten
to buy the wrist bands
and he reads two of the books in less than a day

although he thinks
over a month has passed
when I come back the next day
to give him the chocolate and the E-string
I'll have forgotten to give him the day before,

and then he's started playing the guitar again
even though he's still so ashamed –
I can't help screaming –
and it throbs and tears at his wounds.

Christiansminde, Svendborg, 13th April 2006

he sat here close
to where I am now
and most thoughts arrive
like this,

at least in pairs,
the majority really
without a centre, without

entrances, without
announcing themselves
at all.

The seagulls slit the air
and on the tarmac border separating the path and the water,
two drakes, each missing a leg,
are fighting a third duck whose tail feathers
no longer grace its bottom
but the beak belonging to the smallest
of the other two –

they fight over females
and the last crumbs
left on the path

by an old lady whose terrier more or less
manages to eat most of it
before it hits the ground

and out there, the swans shoot across the water
like loose metaphors
like meaningless dogs

in dreams
like anchorless imaginings
like water lilies,
electric and wound up as if for mating
like in spring

although it's still as cold
as if it were January
and I'm on the path

where, forty years ago, my mum,
young and numb with panic,
edged herself around the warm pool of blood
she could never quite wash from the soles
of her new pumps

even though she scrubbed and scrubbed
when she returned to her flat where, later that day,
she cooked the leg of lamb
and its juice
ran across the chopping board

and on like a stream, to the edge of the table
chasing through the air
like pearl drops
of rubies that throw themselves

to the floor in small taps and splashes,
and when she accidentally cut her finger
she was reminded of the smell of blood
in the slaughterhouse on Kogtvedvej (the road just before
    Ranzausminde
on the outskirts of Svendborg) –

the kind of smell that pulls at the nostrils
like rusted locks
and wet, rotten bark, but now in this moment

underneath the trees, everything smells
so naively fresh

of the beech's buds, sea air and Kenzo Jungle
although he's no longer sat on the tree stump over there

on the path a bit further ahead
as he did
because he preferred the stump
to the bench that would rigidly force itself
in underneath his back

so he'd move
before he again got up, and there
a few metres further down
he stood a month ago,

my little brother, taking a piss
with his headphones in (a Christmas gift
three months and twenty days earlier)
wearing his strawberry hat
and the zip of his bag
still carrying the tiger key ring
(the one he bought from the gypsy lady on the street in Barcelona
on a school trip
three years ago).

So here he was, spinning
his long thin body
into dance

although there were no other girls here
but the old lady
(dressed that day in a violet hat
and chequered trousers covered in mud and grass)
out walking her terrier (stuffed full of bread)
by the water's edge, the dog waddling after her
like a corn-fattened duck, although
everyday at home she feeds it gingerbread and sugar cubes, but
    there
he was, my little brother,
mid-dance, humming,

almost in song, the way he only lets himself go
when he is completely separated
and alone, and I'll never
quite know
what it means,

what he's found
when, by the rail tracks
in the woods between the college and my mum's house,
he comes to
one last time, and stays there,
to then gather himself
and stumble home

to my mum, but here a month ago
on the path in Christiansminde
my little brother zipped up,

picked up his mobile again
and placed it in the pocket of his strange rust-red trousers
(so big that, come June, he'll lose them
in customs at Charles de Gaulle
having to take his belt off in the metal detector
to travel on to New York)
before he walked down to the private pier with the iron gate
to sit

with his feet submerged
in the water, that now too
reflects a sky
on fire

and I wonder
how the tree tops, the birds, the clouds and the human
face
he then too carried so beautifully, so perfectly,
would've looked

from the other side
of the water's surface if he let himself slip
down with his back to the bottom
nearing it without looking
drifting … disappearing …

I pull away in the dusk
and walk home along the rail tracks, cross them, then
walk behind the hospital, past the college, across the railway again
and into the woods and here,
right here
where the path breaks,
he'll four months later in August

find his mobile,
and although it'll be broken and scattered in five pieces
it still works

when he switches it back on
and receives my message dated 13th July 7.34.16 am
which I wrote because I didn't think it was fair
that he'd just written:

"I'm hidden away near the college somewhere
between Svendborg Station and West Svendborg –
I don't know if I'm dead and already in heaven,
but I'm at least in green", unless

something had happened that truly
was real, and he can tell how afterwards
I tried to call him

over twenty times, because I knew it,
although I really didn't know
anything at all,

but I know this, and seven hours later
I'm pacing Kastellet
before my mum calls me to tell me
what I know

he's just done
although I don't know anything at all,
and then I run
into the crossing at Grønningen, and only a few days later
when my mum can almost
speak normally again

will he start to smell
like himself again and not just of hospital chemicals
and the unfamiliar, damp,
stuffy and chalk-white duvet.

Rue de Provence, May 2006

and although it's only two months away,
it's still not possible
to unearth

the butterfly
that right now, in some other place,
flutters its left wing

just fiercely enough
for the dust to soar
onto my white coat

and less than two hours ago,
I stood in the metal detector
where, a month from now, my little brother
will drop his trousers

and by this time too
the sun will flicker
on the floor of Gare de L'Est (where I stood, fifteen minutes ago,
right before I ran to catch the metro either towards Bobigny
or towards Saint-Rémy-lés-Chevreuse
to arrive at Luxembourg by Place Edmond Rostand

before I could turn down rue de Médicis
and further down rue de Vaugirard and into Jardin de
    Luxembourg
by the palace, to then enter the museum

where thirteen months and three days ago,
my little brother and I saw an exhibition
on the self-portraits of great painters

and I took a photo of the painting by
Dali (mostly because of the beard
whose pointy ends stretch beyond
the edges of his averted head,
its face appearing

in the mirror on the other side
of the sitter's body
with the beard fully extended
into its glorious shape)

before we hurried out
and placed ourselves amidst spring on the grass
and my little brother rolled a fag,

its smell, overwhelming
and intense, unfolding

towards me, and also then, in that moment of us,
it was almost too overwhelming
for me to be near ill

with tenderness and all the same so blessed
with all that's him and as beautiful
as blood-red, snow-white
and ebony

that, at times,
it's unbearable
like everything in the ninth arrondissement

(where I'm travelling to
instead of heading to Jardin du Luxembourg).

I settle on a bench
at place d'Estienne d'Orves and wait for
someone to call, for
something to happen,
the same way,

in a month (at my own birthday party), I'll
feel like dancing
and when I'm finally asked
I can't manage it
even though nothing's really wrong, but my legs
won't move properly
and there are scratches on the record
as if time too wishes
to stop or skip
just a few months ahead

the way it perhaps felt too on New Years Eve
two years, five months and thirteen days ago
when he purposefully fell asleep
with his bare feet
in a stream
in the middle of the forest

behind Christian's parents' house
where he'd celebrated New Year with the boys,
and perhaps too, six months later when he cut those scars
that, in July, two months from now (exactly
a month after my birthday party,

where, instead of dancing, I fell down the stairs,
landed on the floor and tore the palm of my hand)
out on a massive bender,
he'll use as templates
while in my sleep

I lie with so much weight
on my left arm
that I can't find it again

when I wake up a few hours later
to the sound of his text,
that he's sent somewhere from heaven
in green,
an hour and a half before
he finally gives up and goes home all
smeared in himself
but right now as I place myself on the bench
here alone in the light
in the Paris spring, he's in Svendborg
sat in Krøyer's garden waiting
for some of the others to bother playing hacky-sack again,
and here on the pavement

right in front of me
it could be us walking, smiling
almost like children
dressed in new patent shoes
and woollen blue spring coats:

I could be carrying the notebook under my arm
that I'll be buying in Printemps in an hour
(where I'll enter because I give in
to my addiction to sterile perfumeries
in shopping centres)

and he could walk right there next to me
trumpet in hand
and the music sheets peering

out of the leather bag slumped
on the left shoulder of a passing stranger,
and next week

we could stay at a summerhouse
somewhere in Provence

to eat Aix-peppered hare
after spending all afternoon
by the neighbour's pool, glistening
in our swimwear
in the sun,
consumed by a summer
which will soon arrive
in such perfect balance
as he'd be

living in Provence, crossing
into that gentleness
he found here

when at the age of seven,
groggy with heat,
but full of the clarity
of a spring, he disappeared
without being either too emaciated,
too unsettled
or too consumed
by the polar ice or the population growth

or by incessantly chasing
some form of tangible
relief,
of comfort,

and the beaches where, in previous summers,
we'd sail and pull our boat onto,
are now slowly swallowed.

They are slowly changed
in tidal stages, with each flow

while temperatures and the average age
rise and rise and soon

Christiania will be torn down, before
the great white thighs of the national handball girls roll around
in jubilation because they've once again won the world cup

and now it's only two months before
he fortunately gives up finding
anything
in the sort of thing
you only need more
and more and more of

and instead
sticks to beer and gin to the extent
he's capable of, even though in two months
he'll still truly need
to attempt
to escape entirely,

and then it'll only be a few days until
I wonder what on earth
it is

that makes him
tell me,
with a transparent smile,
that he'll never attempt
it again.

Islands Brygge, 13th June 2006

in my five-metre dive a moment ago
I lost my bikini,
before I now hit
then break through

the surface. I only manage
to catch the bottoms with my right big toe
and put them on
before I reappear,

between oily lifeguards, teenage boys
and girlfriends with wet bodies
in cut-off denim shorts and their bathing suits pulled down,
at the very same moment that my little brother accidentally
kicks the hacky-sack into Helena Christensen's face
as she's having breakfast in Central Park
with her son and friends, all relaxed and lovely,

and although she smiles sweetly and smells
of ginger and a bit
of apples, apricots and vanilla,
he can't help thinking
how greasy she really looks

and he thinks of the night
two years and a few days ago
when he danced with Nina Persson
and she danced
even more beautifully than she sings,
but to him these particular kinds of infatuations
are nothing more
than a slight discomfort
in the long run,

and then I climb out of the pool
and back onto the diving platform to jump
one last time before I go upstairs to pack my things

and today
is my twenty-sixth birthday, and today

he'll once again happen to drink two and a half litres of gin
and stagger around strangers
on strange streets, almost

hermetically closed off like that time last November
when he visited me and (after the party)
disappeared and I ran around the city all morning
picking up bits of him: there

the strawberry hat, there a shoe and there a sock,
a sweater, a scarf and finally
on the pavement in front of me, the dirty,
flowery rucksack leaning against the post office in Købmagergade
with him attached, asleep
so I gently have to drag him home

and perhaps
one day we'll die
in the same moment, but right now
it's only a month until his secrets are set alight
after, senseless, brave, almost
homeless and all alone, he means
what he's about to do

and without knowing
how lonely he really is,

he wants the woods,
with his carefully considered provisions on his back,
even though on his way out the door
at 4.57 am (where shortly after I wake in Copenhagen thinking
I've wet myself)
he bumps into our mum in the kitchen
(she's up because the cat
once again brought a dead bat into her bed)
who once again notices

that, like so many other times,
he's drunk himself beyond recognition,
beyond himself,

and although she thinks
that she believes he's up
because he's going back to Andreas's party,
she can't go back to sleep

and when Andreas (just as paralytic)
finally rings the door after running all the way to her
because he (like I) has received the text,

they walk to the woods together
and when they've looked for my little brother
for an hour and nineteen minutes,
he's finally (after lying by the tracks
for three hours and seventeen minutes)
returned home

and this is how she finds him:
naked, washing himself, his clothes
already in the laundry basket
even though he still stumbles and shakes
because he's cold

and still tamed by the fear,
and only when she takes his hand
to lead him to bed, does she notice
what he's done,
but he won't

come with her for stitches, although four hours later
he'll have six on his left wrist
and nine on his right, but right now

he's still in Central Park playing hacky-sack with Mike
before he takes the photograph of the small brown sparrow
that he'll use as a postcard and send to me tomorrow
as a belated birthday present.

Langelinie, 13th July 2006

I'm not
watching the ships,
but those dinghies we right now
couldn't have sailed, while

summer, so exceptional and haughty,
has comfortably and lazily entered
everything,
and now it's twelve hours since I still slept
(in the bed at 2nd floor, 9 Store Kannikestrœde), when the sun,
as if to ignite his eyes and force them open,
had already risen; I think it rose as
if to search for him
and perhaps guide him home
through the small dazzling pieces of bait

it placed on the flower buds and tree tops and also
so delicately there on the tree bark and the insects around he
who lay, being the human being

in the bushes on the small slope
a few metres from the tracks, concealed
by the woods
so close

to my mum's house
that she would've heard him
if he'd given up

and I wonder how he really felt,
what it was like to be some place between
or perhaps entirely beside
your own body,

and today it's less than a week since
we ate strawberries on my mum's terrace
so as not to forget again this year
to eat them with cream, and now
it's less than ten hours since
Andreas started yelling, so
that the girls started skipping, so
that the train stormed past close enough

for the passengers to almost catch
the long and wretched
white and red
body,

and finally he awoke
just enough to focus
his gaze
on the deep incisions

he'd cut
into his own wrists
again and again

because the blood kept coagulating,
and as he lay there,
it'd been a few hours

since he started the cutting
and again and again
he cut,
and now,

as I'm wandering around by the little mermaid,
it's only nine and a half hours since
he finally stumbled out of the bushes
and everything once again dissolved
as, trembling, he staggered from tree to tree
out of the woods, out

into the light on the path where a man was walking his fat dog
while I, in my nightie, tried to call him for the eighteenth,
nineteenth,
twentieth time so

that the dog lifted its heavy ears
because it could hear
the faint ringing
from the spot inside the woods

and it lifted its nose
to the air as if to the stumbling lonely figure,
there a bit further ahead so pale and grey
that it was almost blue,

walking
towards them – finally
returning home

where the cat (before my mum shortly after
got him up again, into the car
and to the emergency room) thirty eight minutes later
jumped up and settled onto Schade's *Selected Poems*
placed on top of *The Collected Works of Emily Dickinson*, both
   turned
approximately to the centre pages
right next to him
returned to his bed now,
silent and consumed

by the notes of Sparklehorse,
his hands
with the cuts
gathered at less risk
underneath his chin,
there underneath his mouth carrying a faint smile
which flickered slightly because,

shortly after, he really broke down,
gave in
to that quiet, helpless weeping.

17 Louisenlund, 14th July 2006

(The photograph's been taken on the 13th November 1986 and so is about twenty years and five months old. I'd forgotten all about it but here it is in front of me on my mum's kitchen floor. She must've dropped it from her wallet when she checked for her driving license.)

1: My little brother

He's wearing his light blue overalls and the t-shirt with navy-blue and bottle-green stripes. He's all light and looks like a small warm flame or a paper angel that smells of child and only faintly of piss. You can't tell that he's thinking of all the things the bushes whispered to him that morning while I could only hear their soft movements in the wind.

He's on my lap pulling his face into the most manic expressions he knows. Outside the camera's reach, most of his Playmobil Eskimos are spread across the floor, the majority of them decapitated, and one of the igloos has broken into five pieces because he dropped it when, eagerly looking for someone to show the new village, he fell over the door frame and landed in the middle of the settlement like an improbable catastrophe, scraping his palms and his knees.

I can tell by my face above his, and by my arms holding him in that tight big-sisterly grip, that just before my mum pressed the release and the flash went off, I could feel the small fingers on his left hand press into my thigh and I can tell that I'm struggling to hold back the laughter, consumed with pride and a feral joy.

Only now do I notice that you can already see it, how in this photo too he frowns and tightens his lips in that unusual pose that I now know means he's disturbed by something that'll never be spoken because he's entirely alone with something that can't be spoken. Only in twenty and a half years (now yesterday) will he get close to vocalising it, and at that time when it's finally revealed, this is the expression he'll carry, because again he'll try his best to keep the terror of what's just happened at bay, because desperate and lost to himself, he's finally gathered enough courage to try to make it stop.